A selection of words and music fro[m]
written and transc[r]
by

John L. Bell
&
Graham Maule

G000165538

CONTENTS

All the above songs are recorded by
the Wild Goose Worship Group on an
accompanying tape 'A TOUCHING PLACE'.
Proceeds from these publications will
go towards the MACLEOD CENTRE APPEAL.

Most people divide new songs into three categories:
1) Those which can be sung immediately
2) Those which may be tried after a while
3) Those to be avoided at all costs

You might want to do the same with this collection because it is a cross section of different musical traditions, some of which may be familiar, others quite alien. We suggest you resist this temptation and try all the musical styles.

CONTEMPORARY HYMNS

Three of the songs may be termed 'Contemporary Hymns' in that the music is original and the harmonies differentiate them from hymn tunes of the last century.

In keeping with our other material, these hymns have strongly 'incarnational' words. That means that they speak of the presence of God in all things and particularly celebrate the directness of God as he meets us in Jesus Christ.

This emphasis is in keeping with the tradition of the Celtic Church which arrived in Scotland in the person of Columba who landed on Iona in 563A.D. The missionary zeal of the monks sent out from the settlement on Iona ensured the evangelisation of Scotland, North-East England and parts of the continent of Europe. The songs Columba sent them out with were songs of the nearness of the God of Heaven in the very ordinary things of earth.

FOLK MUSIC

Scotland, in keeping with the other nations in the British Isles, has an immense legacy of folk songs and tunes. They represent the rhythms of working life and leisure time: marches or tramping or weaving or hauling rhythms for the hours of daylight; dance or rocking beats for the evening time.

This is music which is accessible to people of all ages, because many of us will have heard the tunes first on our mother's or grandmother's knee, irrespective of whether we live in the city or on an island. Such items, therefore, need little in the way of teaching, but can be enhanced in their singing when thoughtfully accompanied by a drum, congas or a bodhran.

We have included an English and a French folk tune to avoid any accusation of narrow nationalism.

CHORAL CHANTS

The Taizé Community in France is widely recognised as the source of many contemporary choral chants, of which 'Adoramus Te' and 'Ubi Caritas et Amor' are possibly the best known.

Encouraged by the popularity of these, we have written several, three of which are included in this collection. They are very easy to teach in four parts and very satisfying to sing.

Broadly speaking, we use chants in two ways.
Sometimes we sing them over and over as a means of prayer. Because they are short and have simple words and harmonies, they are easily remembered. It is therefore possible for people to close their eyes and focus their attention on the meaning of the words, offering it to God and, through God, to each other.
Alternatively, we may use them as sung responses to verses of scripture or as contributions (prepared or extempore) in open prayer.
Some people, particularly from reformed traditions, are suspicious of this kind of repetitive singing. Part of that suspicion is due to ignorance – they have never tried it; part is due to blindness – they fail to see the similarity between chants and popular evangelical choruses when sung repeatedly; and part of it is due to the lack of people in the churches who are enthusiastic about new music and new ways of worshipping.

SOUTH AFRICAN SONGS

We include two of these for two reasons.
By singing them, we accept that it is not only Europeans who can produce songs of praise.
By including them in our worship, we show our solidarity with those in South Africa and elsewhere who are the victims of discrimination.
The songs, 'Thuma Mina' and 'Senzenina' have been transcribed from voices. There are many more currently available. A collection of twelve, entitled 'FREEDOM IS COMING' is available in music and on tape (performed by a Swedish Group) from the Iona Community, the sole distributor for the U.K.
Enquiries regarding these and other materials for worship should be addressed to Duncan and Marlene Finlayson, The Abbey Shop, Iona Abbey, Isle of Iona, Argyll PA76 6SN (Tel. 06817-404). For bulk supplies at wholesale rate for church bookstalls, conferences or commercial bookshops please contact Michael Lee, Morning Mist, Horsecombe Vale, BATH BA2 5QR (Tel. 0225-837313).
It is our hope that these songs, which represent a fraction of the music currently used by the Community on Iona and on the mainland, will both enliven the worship of God's people and be an incentive to others to sing new songs to the Lord.

John Bell
Graham Maule
Glasgow, February 1986.

DANCE AND SING, ALL THE EARTH
(Tune: Pulling Bracken)

DANCE AND SING, ALL THE EARTH, GRA-CIOUS IS THE HAND THAT TENDS YOU:

LOVE AND CARE EV-ERY-WHERE GOD ON PUR-POSE SENDS YOU.

Shoot-ing star and sun-set shape the dra-ma of cre-a-tion;

Light-ning flash and moon-beam share a com-mon de-ri-va-tion.

CHORUS: DANCE AND SING, ALL THE EARTH,
GRACIOUS IS THE HAND THAT TENDS YOU:
LOVE AND CARE EVERYWHERE
GOD ON PURPOSE SENDS YOU.

1. Shooting star and sunset shape
   The drama of creation;
   Lightning flash and moonbeam share
   A common derivation.

2. Deserts stretch and torrents roar
   In contrast and confusion;
   Tree tops shake and mountains soar
   And nothing is illusion.

3. All that flies and swims and crawls
   Display an animation
   None can emulate or change
   For each has its own station.

4. Brother man and sister woman,
   Born of dust and passion,
   Praise the one who calls you friends
   And makes you in his fashion.

5. Kiss of life and touch of death
   Suggest our imperfection:
   Crib and womb and cross and tomb
   Cry out for resurrection.

WITH THE ACCOMPANIMENT OF DRUMS, CONGAS OR A BODHRAN, OR MERELY TO
THE TAPPING OF FEET, THIS LIVELY CELEBRATION OF THE CREATED WORLD
IS GOOD TO USE AT THE BEGINNING OR ENDING OF AN EVENT AND A SIMPLE
DANCE MOVEMENT CAN BE PUT TO THE FOLK TUNE.

I AM FOR YOU

1. Before the world began
   One Word was there;
   Grounded in God he was,
   Rooted in care;
   By him all things were made,
   In him was love displayed,
   Through him God spoke and said,
   'I AM FOR YOU'.

2. Life found in him its source,
   Death found its end;
   Light found in him its course,
   Darkness its friend;
   For neither death nor doubt
   Nor darkness can put out
   The glow of God, the shout:
   'I AM FOR YOU'.

3. The Word was in the world
   Which from him came;
   Unrecognised he was,
   Unknown by name;
   One with all humankind,
   With the unloved aligned,
   Convincing sight and mind:
   'I AM FOR YOU'.

4. All who received the Word
   By God were blessed;
   Sisters and brothers they
   Of earth's fond guest.
   So did the Word of Grace
   Proclaim in time and space
   And with a human face,
   'I AM FOR YOU'.

THE WORDS OF THIS SONG ARE A PARAPHRASE OF THE PROLOGUE TO ST. JOHN'S GOSPEL.

GOD ON EARTH
(Tune:O Waly Waly)

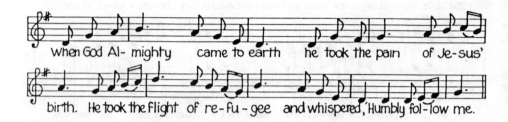

when God Al-mighty came to earth he took the pain of Je-sus'
birth. He took the flight of re-fu-gee and whispered, 'Humbly fol-low me.

1. When God Almighty came to earth,
   He took the pain of Jesus' birth,
   He took the flight of refugee
   And whispered, 'Humbly follow me'.

2. When God Almighty went to work
   Carpenter's sweat he didn't shirk,
   Profit and loss he didn't flee
   And whispered, 'Humbly follow me'.

3. When God Almighty walked the street
   The critic's curse he had to meet,
   The cynic's smile he had to see
   And whispered, 'Humbly follow me'.

4. When God Almighty took his place
   To save the sometimes human race,
   He took it boldly on a tree
   And whispered, 'Humbly follow me'.

5. When God Almighty comes again
   He'll meet us incognito as then,
   And though no words may voice his plea
   He'll whisper, 'Are you following me?'

THIS SIMPLE SONG IS BEST WHEN SUNG SIMPLY. A SOLO VOICE, PAUSING
BETWEEN VERSES FOR A SHORT SILENCE, CAN ENABLE IT TO BE USED AS A
MEDITATION ON JESUS' LIFE. SLIDES OR MIME CAN EASILY BE FOUND OR
DEVISED TO ACCOMPANY IT.

BEHOLD THE LAMB OF GOD

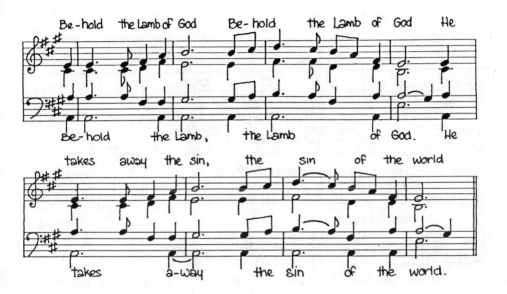

Behold the lamb of God,
Behold the lamb of God;
He takes away the sin,
The sin of the world.

IT IS POSSIBLE TO SELECT PASSAGES FROM OLD TESTAMENT PROPHECY AND
THE STORY OF THE GOSPELS WHICH MAY BE INTERSPERSED WITH THE
SINGING OF THIS CHANT.

THE FOLLOWING MAY BE USEFUL:

ISAIAH 42 v 1 - 4

ISAIAH 52 v 13 - 53 v 6

LUKE 23 v 26 - 49

JOHN 21 v 15 - 17

ALTERNATIVELY, SINGLE VERSES DEPICTING JESUS IN THE MANGER, IN THE
DESERT, HEALING, CRYING, AT PRAYER, AMONG THE UNDESIRABLES ETC.
MAY BE PUT INTO A SEQUENCE AND THE CHANT SUNG BEFORE EACH NEW
IMAGE

WILL YOU COME AND FOLLOW ME?
(Tune: Kelvingrove)

1. Will you come and follow me
   If I but call your name?
   Will you go where you don't know
   And never be the same?
   Will you let my love be shown,
   Will you let my name be known,
   Will you let my life be grown
   In you and you in me?

2. Will you leave your self behind
   If I but call your name?
   Will you care for cruel and kind
   And never be the same?
   Will you risk the hostile stare
   Should your life attract or scare
   Will you let me answer prayer
   In you and you in me?

3. Will you let the blinded see
   If I but call your name?
   Will you set the prisoners free
   And never be the same?
   Will you kiss the leper clean,
   And do such as this unseen,
   And admit to what I mean
   In you and you in me?

4. Will you love the 'you' you hide
   If I but call your name?
   Will you quell the fear inside
   And never be the same?
   Will you use the faith you've found
   To reshape the world around
   Through my sight and touch and sound
   In you and you in me?

5. Lord, your summons echoes true
   When you but call my name.
   Let me turn and follow you
   And never be the same.
   In your company I'll go
   Where your love and footsteps show,
   Thus I'll move and live and grow
   In you and you in me.

EACH OF THE FIRST FOUR VERSES REFLECTS WHAT JESUS ASKS OF US.   IT
MAY THEREFORE BE FITTING TO SING THESE SOLO WITH, IF APPROPRIATE,
A HUMMED HARMONY ACCOMPANIMENT. THEN ALL CAN SING THE LAST VERSE
IN UNISON AS A RESPONSE TO HIS CALL.

'SENZENINA' AND 'SONOSETU' REPRESENT THE FIRST TWO VERSES OF A
BLACK SOUTH AFRICAN SONG. THEY MEAN 'WHAT HAVE WE DONE? WHAT IS
OUR SIN?' THERE IS A THIRD VERSE WHICH MEANS 'WE ARE BLACK'. WE
OMIT THE WORD HERE, SUGGESTING THAT THE THIRD VERSE MAY BE HUMMED
AS A SIGN THAT WE EMPATHISE BUT, BEING WHITE EUROPEANS, CANNOT
PRETEND TO FULLY UNDERSTAND.

Watch, watch and pray,
Jesus will keep to his word.

THIS CHANT IS VERY EFFECTIVELY USED TO HELP PEOPLE MEDITATE ON THE WORDS AND PROMISES OF JESUS. THE BEATITUDES (MATTHEW 5 V 3 - 10) PROVIDE A GOOD EXAMPLE.

IT IS ALSO POSSIBLE TO TAKE A NUMBER OF VERSES FROM DIFFERENT PARTS OF THE GOSPELS AND USE THEM IN A MEDITATIVE SEQUENCE.

E.G.

JESUS SAYS 'I AM THE VINE AND YOU ARE THE BRANCHES'

JESUS SAYS 'ASK AND YOU WILL RECEIVE; SEEK AND YOU WILL FIND;
          KNOCK AND THE DOOR WILL BE OPENED TO YOU'.

JESUS SAYS 'WHOEVER COMES TO ME, I WILL NEVER TURN AWAY'.

JESUS SAYS 'LISTEN, I AM WITH YOU ALWAYS,
          EVEN TO THE END OF THE WORLD'.

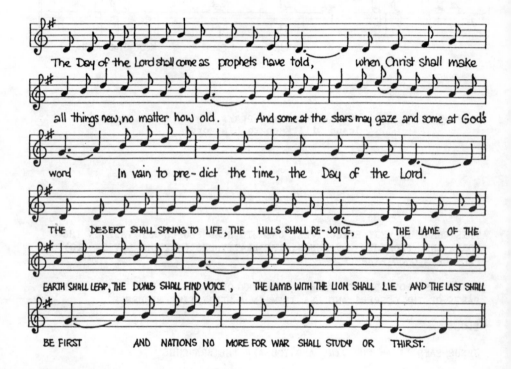

The Day of the Lord shall come as prophets have told, when Christ shall make all things new, no matter how old. And some at the stars may gaze and some at God's word In vain to pre-dict the time, the Day of the Lord.

THE DESERT SHALL SPRING TO LIFE, THE HILLS SHALL RE-JOICE, THE LAME OF THE EARTH SHALL LEAP, THE DUMB SHALL FIND VOICE, THE LAMB WITH THE LION SHALL LIE AND THE LAST SHALL BE FIRST AND NATIONS NO MORE FOR WAR SHALL STUDY OR THIRST.

THE DAY OF THE LORD
(Tune: Air Falalalo)

1. The Day of the Lord shall come
   As prophets have told,
   When Christ shall make all things new
   No matter how old;
   And some at the stars may gaze
   And some at God's word
   In vain to predict the time,
   The Day of the Lord.

2. The Day of the Lord shall come:
   A thief in the night;
   A curse to those in the wrong
   Who think themselves right;
   A pleasure to those in pain
   Or with death at the door;
   A true liberation for
   The prisoners and poor.

CHORUS: THE DESERT SHALL SPRING TO LIFE,
THE HILLS SHALL REJOICE;
THE LAME OF THE EARTH SHALL LEAP,
THE DUMB SHALL FIND VOICE;
THE LAMB WITH THE LION SHALL LIE
AND THE LAST SHALL BE FIRST
AND NATIONS NO MORE FOR WAR
SHALL STUDY OR THIRST.

3. The Day of the Lord shall come
   And judgement be known,
   As nations, like sheep and goats,
   Come close to the throne.
   Then Christ shall himself reveal
   Asking all to draw near
   And see in his face all faces
   Once ignored here.

4. The Day of the Lord shall come
   But now is the time
   To baffle earth's wisdom
   With Christ's folly sublime –
   By loving the loveless,
   Turning the tide and the cheek,
   By walking beneath the cross
   In step with the weak.

THE TUNE, 'AIR FALALALO' SETS PEOPLE'S FEET TAPPING AS A HEALTHY
AND ADEQUATE ACCOMPANIMENT TO THE SINGING. AS WITH OTHER SONGS,
EVERYBODY APPRECIATES THE WORDS MORE AND PARTICIPATES MUCH BETTER
IF EITHER SOLOISTS OR GROUPS (e.g. MEN, WOMEN, BOYS, GIRLS) TAKE A
VERSE AND ALL JOIN IN THE CHORUS.

come, Holy Spirit,   come, heavenly dove,
come, source of renewal,   come, pregnant with love.

Ve - ni sancte spir- it-us,   ve - ni sancte spir-it-us.

speak, speak to our sadness   Christ's word of re-lease

plant seeds for our Freedom   bring heal-ing and peace.

VENI, SANCTE SPIRITUS

RESPONSE: VENI, SANCTE SPIRITUS,
              VENI, SANCTE SPIRITUS,
              VENI, SANCTE SPIRITUS,
              VENI, SANCTE SPIRITUS.

Descant: Come, Holy Spirit,
           Come, heavenly dove,
           Come, source of renewal,
           Come, pregnant with love.

1. Speak, speak to our sadness
   Christ's word of release;
   Plant seeds for our freedom,
   Clear pathways for peace.

2. Find, find in our lostness
   True signs of our worth,
   Raw proof of the saltness
   Sent, meant for the earth.

3. Fire, fire in the darkness
   New flame for the soul;
   Light lamps for our growing
   From broken to whole.

THIS SONG IS BEST SUNG WITH THE CONGREGATION OR LARGER GROUP
SINGING THE RESPONSE, A SMALLER GROUP SINGING THE VERSES AND ONE
OR TWO INDIVIDUALS SINGING THE DESCANT OVER THE RESPONSE.

BALUBALOW

Oh my deir hert, young Je-sus sweit, pre-pair thy cred-dil in my spreit. And

Ba - lu, ba - low, ba - lu, ba - low, ba-

I sall rock thee tae my hert and nev-er mair from thee — de-part.

lu, ba - low, ba - lu, ba - lu, ba - low.

1. Oh my deir hert, young Jesus sweit,
   Prepair thy creddil in my spreit
   And I sall rock thee tae my hert
   And never mair from thee depart.

2. But I sall praise thee ever mair
   With sangis sweit unto thy gloir.
   The knees of my hert sall I bow
   And sing a richt Balubalow.

THE WORDS, VARIOUSLY SPELT, COME FROM AN ANCIENT LULLABYE TO THE
BABY JESUS. IN THIS TWO-PART SETTING, THE MALE VOICES SHOULD MAKE
A GENTLE ROCKING SOUND.

O LAMB OF GOD

O Lamb of God,
You take away the sin of the world;
O Lamb of God,
You take away the sin of the world;
Have mercy, have mercy,
Have mercy on us.

THIS SETTING OF THE 'AGNUS DEI' IS ONE OF FOUR LITURGICAL PIECES WHICH INCLUDE A KYRIE, SANCTUS AND BENEDICTUS. IT IS MEANT PRIMARILY FOR USE AT THE CELEBRATION OF HOLY COMMUNION, BUT MAY BE USED ON OTHER OCCASIONS, FOR EXAMPLE DURING A PRAYER OF CONFESSION OR BETWEEN VERSES OF THE PASSION STORY.

TRAVELLING THE ROAD TO FREEDOM

1. Travelling the road to freedom,
   Who wants to travel the road with me?
   Feted by noise and branches
   And banners hanging from every tree;
   Cheered on by frenzied people,
   Puzzled by what they hear and see:
   Travelling the road to freedom,
   Who wants to travel the road with me?

2. Travelling the road to freedom,
   Who wants to travel the road with me?
   Partnered by staunch supporters
   Who, come the dark, will turn and flee;
   Nourished by faith and patience,
   Neither of which is plain to see:
   Travelling the road to freedom,
   Who wants to travel the road with me?

3. Travelling the road to freedom,
   Who wants to travel the road with me?
   Tipping the scales of justice,
   Setting both minds and captives free;
   Suffering and yet forgiving,
   Even when my friends most disagree:
   Travelling the road to freedom,
   Who wants to travel the road with me?

4. Travelling the road to freedom,
   I am the Way, I'll take you there.
   Choose to come on the journey
   Or choose to criticise and stare.
   Earth's mesmerising evil
   Only a traveller can repair.
   Travelling the road to freedom,
   I am the Way, I'll take you there.

ALTHOUGH REFERRING IN A DIRECT WAY TO PALM SUNDAY, THIS HYMN CAN BE USED AT ANY TIME. IT CAN BE SUNG BY EVERYONE AS A SLOW PROCESSIONAL OR RECESSIONAL, OR IT MAY BE SUNG BY A SMALLER GROUP TO ACCOMPANY MOVEMENT OR SLIDES.

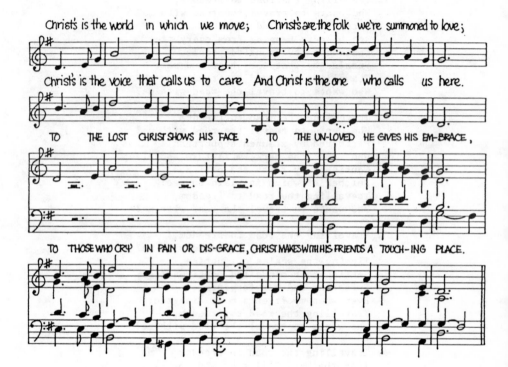

A TOUCHING PLACE
(Tune: Dream Angus)

1. Christ's is the world in which we move,
   Christ's are the folk we're summoned to love,
   Christ's is the voice which calls us to care
   And Christ is the one who meets us here.

   CHORUS: TO THE LOST
             CHRIST SHOWS HIS FACE
         TO THE UNLOVED
             HE GIVES HIS EMBRACE
         TO THOSE WHO CRY
             IN PAIN OR DISGRACE
         CHRIST MAKES, WITH HIS FRIENDS,
             A TOUCHING PLACE.

2. Feel for the people we most avoid –
   Strange or bereaved or never employed;
   Feel for the women and feel for the men
   Who fear that their living is all in vain.

3. Feel for the parents who've lost their child,
   Feel for the women whom men have defiled,
   Feel for the baby for whom there's no breast
   And feel for the weary who find no rest.

4. Feel for the lives by life confused,
   Riddled with doubt, in loving abused;
   Feel for the lonely heart, concious of sin,
   Which longs to be pure but fears to begin.

THIS SONG IS FREQUENTLY USED AT HEALING SERVICES AS PEOPLE COME
FORWARD TO HAVE HANDS LAID ON THEM. THEN, OR AT OTHER TIMES, IT IS
BEST SUITED TO ONE SOLO VOICE SINGING THE VERSES AND ALL JOINING
IN THE CHORUS. EVEN IF PEOPLE THINK THEY KNOW 'DREAM ANGUS' IT IS
AS WELL TO CHECK. THE END OF THE SECOND MUSICAL PHRASE IN THE
CHORUS OFTEN CATCHES PEOPLE OUT.

Jesus Christ is wait - ing, wait - ing in the streets;
no-one is his neigh - bour, all a - lone he eats.

lis - ten, Lord Je. - sus I am lonely too;

make me, friend or stran - ger, fit to wait on you.

JESUS CHRIST IS WAITING
(Tune: Noel Nouvelet)

1. Jesus Christ is waiting,
   Waiting in the streets;
   No one is his neighbour
   All alone he eats.
   Listen, Lord Jesus,
   I am lonely too.
   Make me, friend or stranger,
   Fit to wait on you.

2. Jesus Christ is raging,
   Raging in the streets
   Where injustice spirals
   And real hope retreats.
   Listen, Lord Jesus,
   I am angry too.
   In the kingdom's causes
   Let me rage with you.

3. Jesus Christ is healing,
   Healing in the streets;
   Curing those who suffer,
   Touching those he greets.
   Listen, Lord Jesus,
   I have pity too.
   Let my care be active,
   Healing just like you.

4. Jesus Christ is dancing,
   Dancing in the streets
   Where each sign of hatred
   His strong love defeats.
   Listen, Lord Jesus,
   I feel triumph too.
   On suspicion's graveyard
   Let me dance with you.

5. Jesus Christ is calling,
   Calling in the streets,
   'Come and walk faith's tightrope,
   I will guide your feet.'
   Listen, Lord Jesus,
   Let my fears be few.
   Walk one step before me,
   I will follow you.

A LIVELY AND HAPPY RHYTHM IS BEST FOR SINGING THIS SONG. IT CAN BE SUNG UNACCOMPANIED AND IN UNISON, OR ACCOMPANIED BY A DRUM OR CONGAS IMPROVISING ACCORDING TO THE MOOD OF THE VERSE.

THUMA MINA

1. Thuma mina, thuma mina,
   Thuma mina, Nkosi Yam.

2. Ndiya vuma, ndiya vuma,
   Ndiya vuma, Nkosi Yam.

THIS IS A TRANSCRIPTION OF A BEAUTIFUL SOUTH AFRICAN SONG OF DISCIPLESHIP. THE TWO VERSES MEAN:

SEND ME, JESUS.

I AM WILLING, LORD.

IT IS VERY EASY TO TEACH THE HARMONY AND ONCE PEOPLE SING IT, THEY DON'T FORGET IT. A GOOD TIME TO USE THE SONG IS AT THE END OF A MEETING AS PEOPLE ARE PREPARING TO GO. IT CAN THEN BE USED AS A RECESSIONAL, GETTING LOUDER OR QUIETER AS THE MOOD REQUIRES.